The Trouble with

Tractors

Written by Nicola Baxter · Illustrated by Geoff Ball

ARMADILLO

tractor

farmer

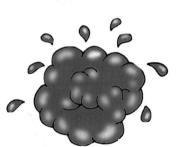

mud

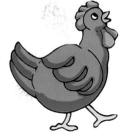

hen

One sunny day, the farmer gets ready to plough the fields.

Brrrrm! Brrrrm! The tractor is ready too.

But in the yard is a big muddy puddle.

Look out, hens!

Published by
Armadillo Books
an imprint of
Bookmart Limited
Registered Number 2372865
Trading as Bookmart Limited
Blaby Road
Wigston
Leicestershire
LE18 4SE

© 2001 Bookmart Limited

Reprinted 2002 (twice), 2004

ISBN 1-84322-120-9

Printed in China

Starting to read – no trouble!

The troublesome tractor in this story helps to make
sharing books at home successful and enjoyable.
The book can be used in several ways to help
beginning readers gain confidence.

You could start by reading the illustrated words
at the edge of each lefthand page with your
child. Have fun trying to spot the same words in
the story itself.

All the words on the righthand pages have already
been met on the facing page. Help your child to
read these by pointing out words and groups of
words already met.

Finally, all the illustrated words can be found
at the end of the book. Enjoy checking all the
words you can both read!

The hens are muddy too!

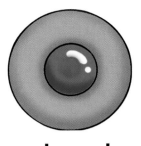

wheel

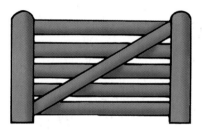

gate

straw

pig

"Sorry, hens!" the farmer calls.

Now there is mud on the tractor's wheels.

They make tracks across the yard.

Oh no! Near the gate is a heap of straw.

Look out, pigs!

Now there is straw on the pigs!

tree

sack

carrots

horse

"Sorry, pigs!" the farmer calls.

Brrrrm! Brrrrm! The tractor goes through the gate.

Its wheels roll over the grass.

Near a tree is a sack of carrots for the horses.

Look out, horses!

The carrots roll over the grass.

hill

"Sorry, horses!" the farmer calls.

There are carrots everywhere!

stream

The tractor rolls down the hill. There is a stream at the bottom.

duck

"Oh no!" calls the farmer.

Look out, ducks!

duckling

Look out, ducklings!

Now there is a tractor in the stream!

water

"Sorry, ducks! Sorry, ducklings!" calls the farmer.

There is water everywhere!

Brrrrm! Brrrrm! The tractor rolls slowly out of the water.

fence

sheep

It chugs up the hill again.

There is a fence to keep the sheep and lambs in.

Look out, sheep!

lamb

The tractor chugs over the fence!

field

cow

"Sorry, sheep! Sorry lambs!" the farmer calls.

In the next field some cows are lying down.

rain

"Oh no," the farmer says. "It's going to rain!"

The cows are chewing grass.

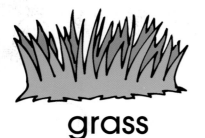

grass

The tractor is going fast.

Look out, cows!

The cows are not lying down now!

cloud

sky

animals

barn

"Sorry, cows!" calls the farmer.

The tractor is ready for work at last. But there is a big grey cloud in the sky.

The animals hurry into the barn.

Look out, tractor!

Here comes the rain!

Look out, animals!
Here comes the tractor!

Picture dictionary

Now you can read these words!

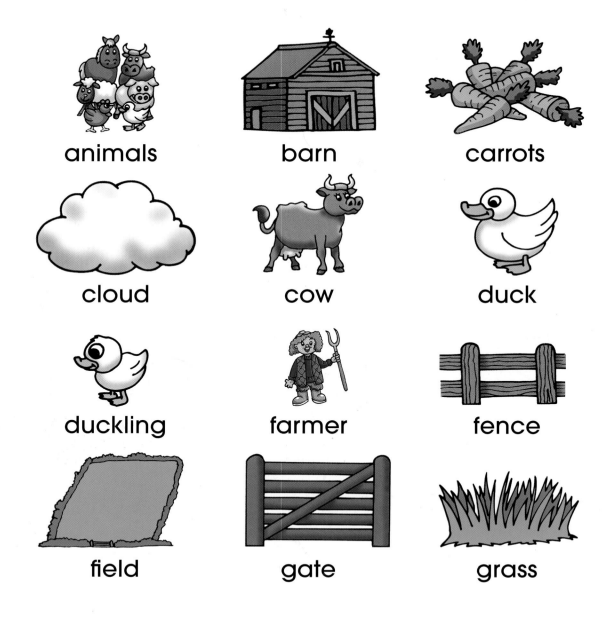

animals

barn

carrots

cloud

cow

duck

duckling

farmer

fence

field

gate

grass

hen

hill

horse

lamb

mud

pig

rain

sack

sheep

sky

straw

stream

tree

water

wheel